Crossroads Multinational
Church of the Nazarene
12229 E. Del Amo Blvd.
Cerritos, CA 90703

Until
We All
Have
Names

2005-2006 NMI
MISSION EDUCATION RESOURCES

❋ ❋ ❋

MISSIONS BOOKS

THE HEART AND LIFE OF HELEN TEMPLE
A Way with Words
by Debbie Salter Goodwin

IN FAITH ON WINGS
Nazarene Mission Aviation
by Timothy R. Eby

THE MASTER'S BUILDER
The Jerome Richardson Story
by Richard Gammill

ROCKETS, REBELS, AND RESCUES
Living the Life of a Missionary Kid
by Mark and Jeanette Littleton

TAKIN' IT TO THE STREETS—AGAIN
Kansas City Rescue Mission
by Joe Colaizzi

UNTIL WE ALL HAVE NAMES
Stories of Medical Missions
by Bill McCoy

❋ ❋ ❋

ADULT MISSION EDUCATION RESOURCE BOOK

MISSIONS NOT SO USUAL
Edited by Wes Eby

Stories of Medical Missions

Until We All Have Names

BILL McCOY

Nazarene Publishing House
Kansas City, Missouri

Copyright 2005
by Nazarene Publishing House

ISBN 083-412-1670

Printed in the United States of America

Editor: Wes Eby
Cover Design: Paul Franitza

10   9   8   7   6   5   4   3   2   1

CONTENTS

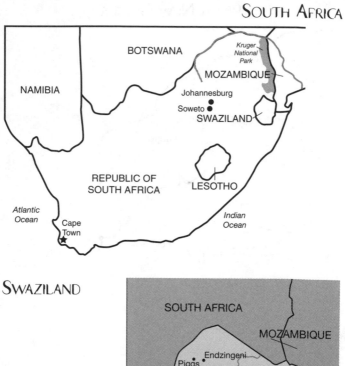

SWAZILAND

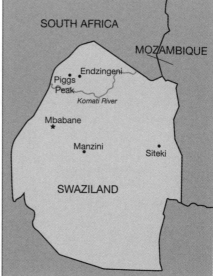

6

Papua New Guinea

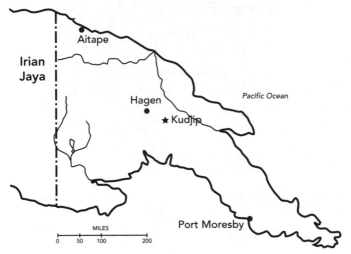

Irian Jaya

Aitape

Hagen

★ Kudjip

Pacific Ocean

Port Moresby

MILES
0   50   100   200

Bill McCoy and his wife, Marsha, have been global missionaries for the Church of the Nazarene for almost two decades. They served in Swaziland from 1985 through 1993 and in Papua New Guinea from 1996 to the present. Dr. McCoy is a physician at the Nazarene Hospital located at Kudjip in the highlands of Papua New Guinea.

Bill was born in Oroville, California. He earned a bachelor's degree from Point Loma College (now Point Loma Nazarene University) in 1975. He received a doctorate in medicine from the University of San Diego in 1980. He completed a residency in family practice at Oral Roberts University in Tulsa, Oklahoma.

Bill and Marsha have three grown children—William Jr., Joshua, and Jennifer.

ACKNOWLEDGMENTS

This book contains the stories of children with illnesses, and some of the lessons those children have taught me, their doctor. The privilege of caring for these kids was granted to me by their parents—for a season—in moments of crisis. These families have shared with me their pain, their tears, their sorrow, their joy. I am deeply grateful to these children and to their parents, especially their mothers, for the trust and confidence they placed in us, in allowing us to care for them and their loved ones.

That privilege also has been mine because of the church. I am deeply grateful to the Church of the Nazarene for providing opportunity and support, for giving me an avenue to fulfill my calling. Medical missions is a team effort, and nothing worthwhile can be accomplished alone. It has been a tremendous honor to serve in mission hospitals in Africa and Papua New Guinea, among the finest servant communities in the world. I have been surrounded by teachers and models, by courage and sacrifice, by heroics and heroes, little noticed in larger circles, but having incalculable impact on my life.

Medical missions is not alone in requiring teamwork. My life, if it is anything positive, is only so because of the many and sustained contributions of friends and family. A special debt of gratitude I owe to my children, who gave their early years to Africa and Papua New Guinea, and especially to my wife,

Marsha, who continues to willingly trade reasonable comforts for the journey we share.

INTRODUCTION

The race appeared to be lost—and I hadn't yet left the starting blocks. Only four months into our first term as missionaries, I stood motionless outside the children's ward of the Raleigh Fitkin Memorial Hospital in Swaziland, unable to enter, mired in despair. Inside were about 60 African children with their mothers, desperate for my help, anxiously awaiting my listening ear, the touch of my hands, a word of hope from my lips. But I was hollow and empty with nothing to offer. Discouragement had overwhelmed me and sapped me of all strength and hope.

I turned away from the ward and, in doing so, abandoned momentarily my professed vocation. I had harbored such high hopes and dreams. I had sat before the mission board and stood before the churches and claimed a clear sense of mission and confidence that God wanted to use me in the role of medical missionary. I had been trained, equipped, affirmed, and sent. What had gone wrong?

Apparently, I was the problem. Patients came to me in large numbers with needs I simply couldn't meet. Not enough knowledge, not enough skill, not enough strength, I sank into depression and self-pity as my failures mounted and my weaknesses revealed themselves.

It was there, in that lowest moment, that a marvelous rescue was offered me. My urine became as Coca Cola, my eyes bright yellow, and I collapsed into bed, overcome by an uninvited "friend" called hepati-

11

Waiting patients at Raleigh Fitkin Memorial Hospital in Swaziland

tis. My already weakening grip on self-sufficiency was pried loose altogether. I verbalized to Marsha, my wife, a complaint about God's sense of humor, that He would allow me to wander so far from home with delusions of significance only to be forced to return in shame and defeat—now punctuated by illness!

Flat on my back with gaze fixed upward, a medical missionary was born. My layers of pride and pretense were peeled away, and I had a new encounter with the Christ who was calling me. No longer would I play the role of saving Africa. It was enough that I had a Savior.

The scope of suffering, whether across the whole of Africa or just within the circle of my community, is immense beyond my mind or abilities, but remains within the boundless compassion of Christ. The response to suffering, likewise, requires the grace and power of God. It became my conscious privilege to simply be an instrument to be used as He wills. As such, successes and failures alike were not mine to own but could be offered up as sacrifices to the only One with a heart big enough to encompass the suffering of this world. After six weeks of hepatitis I was renewed, joyful, grateful; but more than that, I was free.

I have heard an illustration of a child returning stranded starfish from the beach back to the ocean. A realist confronts the effort. "It doesn't matter," he said. "You can't save them all." But the child holds up a single starfish with the response, "It matters to this one."

Early on I pictured myself as the child on the beach. As a medical missionary, I couldn't save them all, so I focused on one patient at a time. In the ensuing years my thinking has changed. I am no longer represented by the child tossing starfish. Rather, I am also one of the starfish. I have lived among thousands of desperate lives struggling for survival, and I have seen many returned safely to the ocean. Since we have shared the beach, and many of them have no voice to speak for themselves, the telling of their stories has fallen to me.

These are stories of sick and injured children, of whom the world is full. So full in fact that our response, on hearing yet another story, may be diminished by fatigue rather than stirred by compassion.

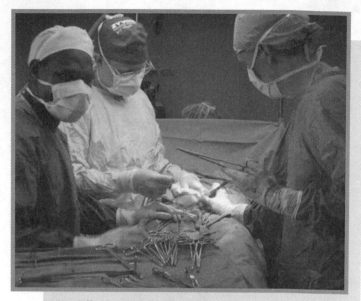

Dr. Bill in emergency room in Swaziland hospital

The sheer volume of suffering patients encountered in a mission hospital has the potential of desensitizing the health-care provider as well.

To illustrate, take this record from my diary of a single day (September 8, 2000):

- rounds on inpatient ward
- dilatation and curettage, two patients
- induction of labor
- postpartum hemorrhage
- long arm cast for fracture
- reduction of finger dislocation
- repair of tendon laceration

- chemotherapy for leukemia
- start two IV lines, one intraosseous line
- lumbar puncture (spinal tap)
- acute bacterial meningitis
- hyperemesis gravidarum
- nephrotic syndrome
- chronic leukemia, blast crisis
- peritoneal tuberculosis
- retained placenta, postpartum hemorrhage, and shock
- Caesarean section for persistent occiput posterior presentation with post-op eclamptic seizure

Every diagnosis and each procedure above represents an encounter with a person, an opportunity to serve and to share. But the list also demonstrates the dangerous potential that a long line of suffering humanity may be reduced to a workload, and a heavy one at that, and one that will repeat itself endlessly day after day.

The risk that our compassion will diminish is real for us—it isn't so for God. Moses in his own strength failed to rescue the Israelites from the Egyptians, so he hid himself in a corner of the desert. It was there that Moses was confronted with the heart of God. "I have indeed seen the misery of my people . . . I have heard them crying out . . . I am

MEDICAL MISSIONS, AT ITS BEST, REFLECTS A DIVINE RESPONSE, RATHER THAN A HUMAN ONE, TO SUFFERING.

concerned about their suffering. So I have come down to rescue them" (Exodus 3:7-8*a*).

God is witness to all the suffering, every wrong inflicted, every injustice incurred, throughout every age in every corner of His creation, and He is neither weary nor uninvolved. Rather, God is full of compassion, committed to rescue, always redeeming. Medical missions, at its best, reflects a divine response, rather than a human one, to suffering.

It is my prayer that these accounts will not dull the readers' hearts but will compel them to embrace those who suffer, as a few of them assume a name and a face. Those faces invariably have had eyes full of tears; often those tears were chased by a smile. The embrace, because Christ is in it, contains healing for those who offer it as well as those who receive it.

Daily, long lines of patients await the services offered by those called into medical missions. There is a tendency among health workers, especially those laboring beneath the strain of a heavy load, to depersonalize, sometimes substituting a number or a diagnosis for a name. This book is an attempt to begin to correct that error. Healing cannot be fully ours *until we all have names.*

I

NELISIWE

"If I find in myself a desire which no
experience in this world can satisfy, the most
probable explanation is that I was made
for another world" (C. S. Lewis).

Even now, after many years of mission hospital
experience, the children's ward would still be a for-
midable challenge. But I was young back then, and
the weight of caring for all those African babies and
sick children seemed almost unbearable. Fifty patients crowded into a long, open room, separated
only by a few small partial dividers. The children's
ward bore no resemblance to the controlled environ-
ment and private rooms of the American hospitals
where I had spent the previous four years.

Morning devotions routinely preceded our
rounds. A senior nurse called us together and provided
an opening for someone to lead us in singing. Years of
arduous training and diligent practice could not pro-
duce a more powerful or moving sound. Fifty mothers,
whose only qualification for this "choir" was their ma-
ternal relationship to a sick or injured child, fell easily
into rich harmonies and complex arrangements that
penetrated deeply into one's soul. It was the music
from the depths of the African experience about
which I knew so little.

In the first cubicle were the two drip tables. Over them hung intravenous solutions, providing fluids for a row of dehydrated babies. Attentive mothers occupied the opposite side, caring for their children and hoping for some reassurance from this young, foreign doctor.

In the second cubicle was an emaciated child curled into a fetal position, too sick to move. Six-year-old Nelisiwe had been admitted during the previous night with a diagnosis of probable malaria, based on a swelling in her left side thought to be an enlarged spleen. The combination of Africa, sick child, and big spleen is usually sufficient to presume malaria.

But the mass didn't feel like a typical spleen, and an ultrasound revealed a large tumor involving the left kidney. I shared the unhappy news with her anxious mother, who had no experience or knowledge of a disease, such as cancer. The following day, we took Nelisiwe to the operating room and removed the mass, known as Wilms' tumor, along with the involved kidney. During surgery it was apparent the tumor had begun to spread in the abdomen and that the operation alone would not effect a cure.

We contacted Dr. Michael Greef, an oncologist (cancer specialist), in the Republic of South Africa (RSA). Nelisiwe needed intensive radiation and chemotherapy, impossible in Swaziland but available at Baragwanath Hospital in the southern part of Soweto on the outskirts of Johannesburg. Dr. Greef and Baragwanath were willing to treat Nelisiwe without cost, if we could transport her to the RSA.

Dr. Zanner with Nelisiwe and her mother preparing to fly to the hospital

Dr. Richard Zanner, director of the Africa Region for the church at that time and also a pilot, was with us in Swaziland on the day the plan unfolded. I went directly to Nelisiwe's mother and asked her to pack her meager belongings as we were leaving momentarily for Matsapa Airport in Manzini. She and Nelisiwe would fly to the RSA in Dr. Zanner's Cessna to an enormous hospital, where Nelisiwe would receive necessary treatment for her cancer.

This mother and child from a small Swazi village had no money, had rarely been in a vehicle, and certainly never dreamed of flying. Baragwanath Hospital was/is the biggest acute-care hospital in the world. Soweto, a conglomerate of townships with more than 3 million residents with a reputation for unrest and violence, embodied all the tensions of those final turbulent months of apartheid. I was amazed at the mother's trust in us and acceptance of this sudden and radical transfer.

The team at Baragwanath Hospital needed the surgical specimen (the kidney and tumor). We packed it in a Tupperware container and handed it to Nelisiwe's mom without disclosing the contents, as she was boarding Dr. Zanner's small plane. To the Swazis, body parts, sometimes retrieved from dead bodies, had powerful spiritual and magical significance. I simply asked this mother to deliver this package to Nelisiwe's doctors upon their arrival.

Nelisiwe and her mother resided at a Ronald McDonald House, a residential facility for cancer victims, taking a shuttle to Baragwanath daily for radiation treatments and chemotherapy. It was a long, difficult month for mother and child, and their desire to return home increased daily. Once Nelisiwe had completed her radiation treatments and an initial course of chemotherapy, she would come back to Swaziland to continue her chemotherapy with us.

When the day came for them to return, my wife, Marsha, made the five-hour drive to retrieve Nelisiwe and her mother. The original plan was to pick them up at the hospital. However, Marsha was late getting there, and the staff had sent a very disappointed Nelisiwe and her mother back to the McDonald House via a hospital shuttle bus. After explaining, an African nurse offered to accompany Marsha through the smoke-filled streets of Soweto.

Marsha pulled up to the residential home simultaneously with the shuttle. As Nelisiwe disembarked from the shuttle, she turned and recognized my wife. Suddenly, she was overwhelmed with joy and excitement. Neither disease nor surgery nor chemotherapy could slow her as she raced to Marsha and threw herself wholeheartedly into my wife's embrace. She was going home!

Nelisiwe and I spent a lot of time together over the following six months. She came with her mother every two to three weeks for chemotherapy, something with which I had no previous experience or training. I followed protocols recommended by Dr. Greef and learned as we proceeded. I knew every vein on Nelisiwe's arms. I can still picture the friendliest of those veins for administering her medicines. Nelisiwe tolerated my shortcomings and accepted her treatments and the side effects with courage and grace. As this beautiful girl fought for her life, I struggled to find myself as a missionary, physician, and friend in a very foreign setting. The trust and confidence I received from Nelisiwe, as well as her obvious dependence on me to give my best effort, helped make me into a better person and care provider. We never saw a recurrence of her cancer.

While I learned something about cancer treatment because of my relationship with Nelisiwe, I

> AS THIS BEAUTIFUL GIRL FOUGHT FOR HER LIFE, I STRUGGLED TO FIND MYSELF AS A MISSIONARY, PHYSICIAN, AND FRIEND IN A VERY FOREIGN SETTING.

Nelisiwe

learned much more than that. Nelisiwe taught me lessons in courage, grace, trust, and perseverance. My favorite memory of Nelisiwe, though, is one that I did not personally witness. It was that moment in the dusk and smoke of Soweto when Nelisiwe turned toward Marsha and home. I understand that yearning for home, the place of peace and security that often eludes us in this life. What Nelisiwe couldn't know was that she was helping me find home even as we were helping her overcome her illness.

2
MABHAYOYO

"When Moses' hands grew tired, they took a
stone and put it under him and he sat on it.
Aaron and Hur held his hands up—one on
one side, one on the other—so that his hands
remained steady till sunset" (Exodus 17:12).

Mabhayoyo's hands were completely and instantly severed at the wrists between the track and
the wheels of the sugar cane-loaded train. He and
his friend had been playing "chicken," the winner being the last to pull back from the railings as the train
bore down upon them. His friend was killed on impact. Mabhayoyo, in addition to losing both hands,
suffered a severe head injury. The farm workers, first
to reach the boy, applied pressure dressings to the
briskly bleeding stumps where hands had once been
and rushed him to the Raleigh Fitkin Memorial Hospital (RFMH) in Manzini, Swaziland.

Upon arrival the boy was comatose without a
measurable blood pressure. We battled a strong sense
of futility. In the remote chance that we could save
his life, it was still unlikely that he could ever return
to any semblance of normal existence. There was a
probability of permanent brain injury and no hope
for his hands. We transfused blood through the veins

23

Mabhayoyo with nurse Simelene

of his legs and rushed to the operating room to close the gaping wounds of his head and forearms.

By the following morning, his condition was significantly improved. He was awake, eyes open, moving all extremities, though weak on one side due to the head injury. Over the next few days his weakness resolved, and there was no remaining sign of brain injury. In fact, the boy we had first encountered in a coma emerged from his injuries with a sparkle in his eyes. He only lacked hands in his determination to resume his life to the fullest.

We began to look into the acquisition of prosthetic hands but discovered that prostheses were not functional or practical for a growing boy in rural Swaziland. Our search eventually led us to Dr. McCasland, an orthopedic surgeon in Johannesburg. Dr. McCasland recommended a surgery developed during World War II in which the two bones of the forearm are separated to create two fingers. Muscles, along with nerve and blood supply, are released, crossed, then reattached to the two bones. Over time patients, especially children, are able to learn to control the rearranged forearm and develop pincer function very similar to that of the normal thumb and index finger. Dr. McCasland was ready to perform the operation; the train company was prepared to cover the costs.

Marsha and I took Mabhayoyo with his most anxious mother into the heart of the intimidating metropolis of Johannesburg. As we entered the bright and modern private hospital, the staff was skeptical that we had come to the right place. In the days of apartheid, how could this poor African family expect service in a top-notch medical facility? The mother, son in her arms, in simple dress and with head bowed, avoided eye contact with hospital personnel as she followed us down the corridor to Mabhayoyo's assigned room. The bright shiny floor, beautiful pictures on the wall, and large comfortable

THIS BOY HAD BEEN RUN OVER BY A TRAIN, YET HE WAS OVERCOMING A MOUNTAIN OF OBSTACLES AS HE EMBRACED A NEW LIFE.

bed with clean white linens only added to her discomfiture.

The tension eased considerably a few moments later when an African nurse, generous in spirit as well as physical presence, warmly welcomed Mabhayoyo and his mother in fluent Siswati. She assured us all—and we did not doubt her—that everything would be fine, and that she would personally see to it that Mabhayoyo and his mother were well cared for. Marsha and I departed in confidence and with gratitude for this angel of mercy who so readily identified and addressed the heartfelt concerns of this Swazi mother and child.

A few days later with the surgery completed, we brought Mabhayoyo and his mother back to Swaziland. We had the great joy of witnessing the miracle as Mabhayoyo learned to use his new right hand. At first, just a hint of movement. Then deliberate and directed. Finally, increasing strength and versatility.

Mabhayoyo would accompany me on my rounds, and he enjoyed reaching into my coat pockets to "steal" my stethoscope. He began to practice writing with a pencil. Eventually he could pick up a coin off a cushioned surface. He joined me in my upstairs office and rearranged my desk. Though he could sometimes be a nuisance, my tolerance was not tested. This boy had been run over by a train, yet he was overcoming a mountain of obstacles as he embraced a new life. Without a hint of self-pity, never an excuse, his play was an inspiration to me. A great spirit was unhindered by a small, broken body.

Given the success of the first surgery, the question arose as to whether we should operate on the left forearm as well. The issue was settled on the day that Mabhayoyo came to me with his request (in Siswati), "Doctor, please do the same thing on my other arm." The second trip to Johannesburg was accomplished with less anxiety as Mabhayoyo and his mother were reunited with a hospital staff that now included many friends of varying skin color. All of them were delighted with the outcome of the earlier surgery and the high-energy boy with the gift for pranks and winning hearts.

The second surgery was equally successful, and Mabhayoyo graduated from Johannesburg and eventually our hospital as well. We placed him in a Catholic school for children with disabilities where he continued to win friends and inspire all who crossed his path.

I visited the school a year later to check on Mabhayoyo. I was surprised to learn he wasn't enrolled for a second year. The sister (nun) told me I shouldn't be shocked. After the first year, Mabhayoyo had returned to the public school near his home. This school was reserved for handicapped children, and Mabhayoyo did not qualify!

3
MAZWI

"And he said to me, 'Son of man,
eat what is before you, eat this scroll;
then go and speak . . .'" (Ezekiel 3:1).

I must confess I have heard many stories similar to the one that follows here. These accounts have each contained their own interesting twists and unique features, but the basic theme is the same. There is a financial need, and just as the crisis moment is imminent, the need is met in a remarkable and unexplainable fashion. The stories tend to strengthen people's faith and hope (that they, too, might be recipients). But I have played the role of skeptic. I have listened to the stories and strove to find the rational explanation, looking for unspoken details to unravel the mystery. In doing so, I played the role of fool.

❊ ❊ ❊

Sunday morning service in the simple mud and stone African church went long by Western standards, but certainly not boring. Spirited music, powerful prayer, and dynamic preaching filled the time and the hearts of the worshipers. Ten-year-old Mazwi sat near the front on the men's side with other boys his age on woven grass mats spread over the dirt floor. The women's side was more colorful, as bright orange uniforms served to strengthen a sense of group identity. Some of the more zealous women had spent the entire night at the church in a vigil of singing and prayer.

The service ended in the hot early afternoon hours. Mazwi started for home on foot, keeping to the dirt road as he had been taught. The African veldt, home of the poisonous puff adder, was not safe for barefoot travelers.

Mazwi may have heard the sound of the approaching vehicle, but it is unlikely that he felt its impact. His head snapped back, shearing the liga-

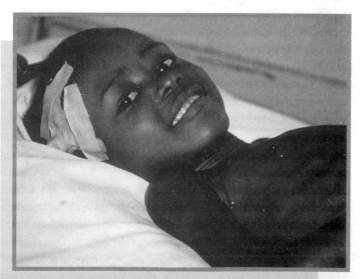

Mazwi in traction for spine fracture

ments and shattering the bones of the upper neck. Bone fragments were driven into the spinal canal, lodging against the cord near the base of his skull.

Examination in the hospital revealed that Mazwi had been paralyzed over the entire left side of his body and had lost sensation on his right side. His situation was extremely precarious. The fracture, high in the cervical spine, was unstable. Even the slightest movement carried a risk of further damage to the spinal cord and a fatal outcome.

Mazwi was placed in neck traction in the first bed in the children's ward, his mother never leaving his side. We couldn't stabilize his fracture, nor could we afford surgery in the Republic of South Africa (RSA). Day after day I made the rounds, looked into mother's eyes, and repeated the same pessimistic litany, "He must not move nor be moved. With any sudden movement, Mazwi might die." Then I would proceed to the next patient. I grew weary of the hopelessness of my own words.

One day the instructions stuck in my mouth before I could utter them. As I approached Mazwi's bed on my rounds, I suddenly turned and left the ward, walked to my office telephone, and after several attempts reached one of the RSA's best neurosurgeons. I told Dr. Plotkin about Mazwi's injury and our predicament. He offered to help, waiving his personal fees, but estimated the operating room costs at 3,000 rand, the equivalent of $1,500.

I returned to the bedside and announced to Mazwi and his mother that we were going to the RSA to have Mazwi's fracture repaired. The woman, having almost no money of her own, expressed her concern about the costs. Her family would never be able to repay $1,500. Unable to muster an adequate response, for I, too, was unsure, I tried to satisfy her with the words, "God will supply our need."

That same evening we met for our weekly prayer meeting in the upstairs portion of our quadriplex in the home of Terry and Mary Newton, our dear friends and colleagues. Mary served as the hospital administrative secretary and had overheard my phone call to Dr. Plotkin. She requested prayer for Mazwi. My wife followed immediately with the simple statement, "And I know where we will get the money."

I was glad for her confidence, but Marsha had no idea how much cost this venture would require. Marsha explained that she had gone to the post office that morning at the time I was telling Mazwi's mother, "God will supply." An unexpected, unsolicited, registered letter had arrived, containing a donation. That was exciting, and I felt it would be a good beginning toward meeting this need.

"How much money, Marsha?" The memory of her answer still sends a chill through me.

"Fifteen hundred dollars," she replied.

Dr. Plotkin repaired Mazwi's cervical fracture. The costs came to precisely $1,500. Mazwi was on his feet, walking soon after the surgery, and regained full use of his arms. The last time I saw him, he had a

Mazwi after surgery

slight limp. That limp never bothered me. The mental image of Mazwi's gait elicits nothing in me but profound wonder and gratitude at the mystery of God's involvement in our lives.

A few years after Mazwi's surgery, I read a brief newspaper article stating that Dr. Plotkin, renowned RSA neurosurgeon, had taken his own life. I do not know what brought him to such despair. I regret that Dr. Plotkin did not sense grace nor goodness sufficient for his own situation. We will always be grateful to him for the instrumental role he played in bringing health and wholeness to Mazwi.

We have served more than 15 years on the mission field. During that period we have received only one letter with a check for $1,500. During that same period I have only once, to my memory, told anyone that God would supply $1,500—readily admitting that my response was not so much a reflection of faith as it was of desperation. I am convinced those two moments occurred in divine synchrony, designed to teach me a valuable lesson in trust.

4

JANE ORR

"This was the appearance of the likeness of the glory of the LORD. When I saw it, I fell facedown, and I heard the voice of one speaking" (Ezekiel 1:28*b*).

I was exhausted as we departed Swaziland for furlough in 1989. We had completed our first four-year term. Long, strenuous hours and sleepless nights had sapped my strength. Violence, abuse, alcoholism, witchcraft, and death had bombarded my senses. I was staggering beneath the weight of Africa's pain.

I felt relief as we boarded our flights for America and harbored doubts whether I could return to Africa after furlough to resume the same pace for another term.

TERMINATION OF OUR MISSIONARY SERVICE SEEMED REASONABLE AND CONSISTENT WITH GOOD STEWARDSHIP.

In addition to my fatigue, our first furlough began with a financial crisis. We had purchased a house in Tulsa, Oklahoma, in 1983, two years before our move to Swaziland. When our assignment to Africa came, we attempted to sell the house, but found ourselves in the middle of a crashing market due to the oil-related economic woes of Tulsa in the mid '80s. Home values bottomed out, and our house hung like a millstone around our necks.

With a mortgage of $75,000 and unable to sell, we attempted to rent our house throughout our first term. Rental income wasn't enough to cover our loan payments, so we depleted our savings. Several months the house sat empty. As we began furlough, our savings gone, we didn't have enough funds to cover even a single month's loan payment.

I was fortunate to be offered work with a medical group in northern California, enabling us to cover our payments. But a long-term solution was needed. How could we return to Africa without making provision for the house payments? Termination of our missionary service, at least for a period of time, seemed reasonable and consistent with good stewardship.

The possibility of interrupting our mission assignment held an additional attraction for me, though I couldn't admit it publicly. The difficulties of the task in Swaziland frightened me, and I was tempted to use our financial obligations as an excuse for remaining in America.

Also, I was *not* unaware of the benefits that my family was enjoying from my employment as a physician in California. Dear friends and colleagues welcomed us into their homes, and I was envious of their houses, their cars, and the lifestyles they could afford. Would it be wrong for my wife and children to enjoy some of the same?

Several months into the furlough, we were invited, along with several other missionaries, to say a few words at the opening of the Sacramento District NMI convention. An enormous crowd packed the auditorium. Trumpets blared as hundreds of colorful balloons fell from the ceiling onto the cheering crowd below. Enthusiasm reached a fevered pitch. I waited my turn to address the convention. My heart was in turmoil; my mind struggled to find appropriate words.

As I stood to speak, my thoughts would not abandon my own struggle. "Tonight in Sacramento we are celebrating the great cause of missions," I began, "and we should. But at this moment at a mission hospital on the other side of the world, it is 6 o'clock in the morning. One of my missionary colleagues is finishing a night on call. He has probably been awake and working for the past 22 hours. He has given his best efforts, often in life-and-death situations. He has saved some patients, and he has lost others. He is covered with his own sweat, and his clothes are stained with the blood and vomit of the patients he has cared for through the night. He is mustering his strength to give his best efforts for the next 10 hours, for there are about 100 patients needing his attention today. Brothers and sisters, it is appropriate that you should celebrate, but I am wondering why I am here on this platform rather than there at his side." It became quiet in the auditorium as people tried to adjust to my somber comments.

In the weeks that followed, my internal debate regarding our future continued. Dr. Russ Tweet, managing partner for the medical group for whom I was working, was encouraging me to make a decision.

Marsha and I needed to settle the issue for our family, and the medical group needed to know as they made plans for their own future.

The breakthrough came in the early spring of 1990. I had just enjoyed lunch with friend and fellow missionary Dan Anderson. Dan had listened to the description of my quandary and shared some wise counsel. I was walking back to the workplace, praying as I walked, when I sensed a renewed call of God on my life. I scribbled a note that I placed on Dr. Tweet's desk, "Thanks so much for your patience with me. I am a missionary. I'm going back to Africa."

A few days after settling the issue about our future direction, Marsha met me as I arrived home from work and told me that Dr. John Crouch had called. He had news for us regarding Jane Orr, a former patient of mine during our years in Oklahoma.

Jane, in her 90s, had severe arthritis of her back and hips and, as a result, was bedridden. She lived in a nursing home near the campus of Oral Roberts University (ORU). Though her joints were terrible, there was nothing wrong with her mind or her spirit. She remained joyful and passionate about life and others, even as she was confined to bed for the last few years of her life.

Dr. Crouch, director of the ORU Family Practice Residency Program where I trained, was—and still remains—both my dear friend and mentor. John became Jane Orr's doctor when we went to Swaziland.

During our furlough year, without our knowledge, Jane Orr told Dr. Crouch that she felt God was leading her to leave money for us. At first she suggested she might leave $10,000. A few days later, however, she revised that figure and told John she was thinking of leaving $25,000.

As Marsha recounted the story to me, I had to sit down. Jane had been a dear patient, but we had never mentioned money in our conversations. She was not aware of our house or the mortgage we owed. Nor was John Crouch. I was groping for an explanation of what I was hearing. What was the reason for this gift? Could this be from God? I felt exposed and vulnerable, fearful in the sudden awareness of a holy Presence.

MY DOUBTING AND COMPLAINING, MY PITIFUL FAITH, MY SELFISHNESS AND SINFULNESS, ALL LAID BARE BEFORE THE ONE WHOSE NAME IS FAITHFUL AND TRUE.

Jane Orr wasn't ready to settle the issue of the money. After more thought and prayer, she summoned Dr. Crouch once again to her bedside. This time she suggested the amount should be $50,000.

John respected Jane's desires, but he wasn't sure she had this much money to give. He contacted Jane's financial manager, a wonderful Methodist man, and informed him of Jane's intentions. The manager was already aware and admitted to John that he had suggested, half in jest, that Jane might consider leaving her money to a Methodist missionary. Jane assured him that she knew what she was doing.

Jane called both her financial manager and Dr.

Crouch one last time. She had settled the issue. This time it was not a suggestion. She would leave $75,000 for us. She was firm regarding this figure and instructed that this amount be designated in her will. Sensing the matter was finished, John Crouch had called to inform us.

Listening to Marsha, it was as if a wave exploded over me, immersing me in emotions both fearsome and joyful. My doubting and complaining, my pitiful faith, my selfishness and sinfulness, all laid bare before the One whose name is Faithful and True. I was overwhelmed with a powerful urge to hide and yet another strong desire to worship.

A few weeks later Jane Orr died and saw her Savior face-to-face. Issues regarding our calling and purpose had been tested and settled. The mortgage on the house was paid, the gates thrown open for our return to the mission field.

5

FRANK JOE

"When I look back at my past and think how much time I wasted on nothing, how much time has been lost in futilities, errors, laziness, incapacity to live; how little I appreciated it, how many times I sinned against my heart and soul—then my heart bleeds. Life is a gift. Life is happiness, every minute can be an eternity of happiness!" (Dostoyevsky, on the day of his reprieve of execution)

Frank Joe had acute leukemia. It could be argued that a patient with leukemia in a developing country with severely limited resources, such as Papua New Guinea, should be offered comfort care only, and that aggressive therapy is inappropriate. The time, energy, and expense necessary to prolong the life of one patient is difficult to justify against the needs of the many. Nevertheless, face-to-face with this six-year-old boy and his parents, listening to their desperate plea for a few more tomorrows with their child, it was nearly impossible to deny them our strongest efforts in treatment.

We explained to the parents, as best we could, the diagnosis and the poor long-term prognosis. We told them about the huge challenges of chemotherapy, including side effects and the necessity of frequent visits

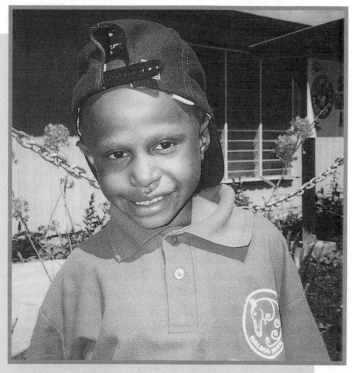

Frank Joe with his ever-present ball cap

and regular admissions to the hospital. To embark on chemotherapy required a major commitment from this family as well as ourselves as caretakers.

Frank was an extremely handsome boy with a perfect, winsome smile, instantly charming everyone he met. His initial trust in us was tested when we began to approach him repeatedly with needles and powerful medicines that invariably caused nausea and vomiting. Frank's hair fell out, and he was left with a smooth scalp that he kept covered with a baseball cap.

Between courses of chemotherapy, Frank felt great. He regained his strength and love for life. On good days, we would stand at opposite ends of the children's ward, pitching a tennis ball back and forth. Our fans were the patients in the other 26 beds and their families, and we put on a grand and glorious show. Curve balls, fast balls, sliders catching the inside corner—all things were possible for Frank Joe. I was simultaneously broadcaster, teammate, and opposing hitter.

We shared moments of ecstasy when Frank robbed me of a grand slam by leaping high over the left field fence (bed 12), and tears flowed freely when a line drive caught Frank between the eyes. As we played throughout every game, I was acutely aware of the stakes. The brevity of time dramatically accentuated the significance of our play, for life itself was being defined by our choices. There was no time for meaningless diversion; all things mattered.

Frank was in Nazarene Hospital at Kudjip over Easter, so we asked him and his mother to join us for dinner in our home. He sat on a fat medical textbook, bringing him closer to his plate, and caught on quickly to the novelty of silverware. Red Jell-O was far too foreign to be tried, but he had no qualms about meat and potatoes. One more meal of similar volume and I believe Frank might have regained the weight he lost as a result of his illness.

Frank's therapy necessitated weekly trips to the hospital to check his blood count and receive intravenous chemotherapy every second or third week. Frank would cry briefly during the needle insertion and administration of the medicine; then when the treatment was completed, his famous smile returned.

His leukemia went into remission for about six months before Frank suffered a relapse. We changed his treatment regimen, trying the remaining options available to us. There was a partial response, but it became apparent that the treatments were only buying a little time and would not cure the disease. It seemed the price of one more smile from this precious boy was exacted in tears. At the end of every visit, I told Frank Joe, "Play every day. Work every day. Laugh every day. Cry a little every day. Pray every day. Always obey your mom—she is God's special gift to you." Frank eventually had the prescription memorized and would finish my litany as soon as I began.

FRANK THEN HURRIED THROUGH THE DOORWAY AND ATTEMPTED TO GET BEHIND THE MIRROR, LOOKING FRANTICALLY FOR THE PEOPLE WHO SO CLOSELY RESEMBLED HIM AND ME!

I was at the computer in my home one afternoon when I heard a child's voice. At first I was unable to discern the words but caught them as I went to answer the door. Frank was calling for me. "Waitman! Waitman! (white man)." Frank was on our

43

front porch—alone. He explained that he was upset with his mother, so he had run away. He had left her in the hospital ward and had come with his mom's knowledge to my house.

I offered Frank a book to entertain himself. He found his place in the middle of the living room, placing the book before him upside down, thumbing through the pages, studying the pictures. I had a new cap for Frank and replaced the old one he was wearing. I led him to the hallway mirror so he could see himself in his new hat. At first glance, his whole body shook with astonishment. He turned and looked at me with wonder, then back to the mirror, then again at me. Frank then hurried through the doorway and attempted to get behind the mirror, looking frantically for the people who so closely resembled him and me.

For two years we battled the leukemia. At the end, Frank Joe developed a severe infection that his immune system could not fight due to his cancer. Treatments were no longer effective, and we released this beautiful boy, who had given us so much joy and laughter, into the waiting arms of Jesus.

I miss Frank Joe. His smile is ever before me. A scribbled note sits on my desk and asks the question I often posed to myself as I gave chemotherapy to this brave young man, "How many tears for a smile?" I came to believe that a sincere smile is a miracle of inestimable value. And Frank and I shared many.

6

LISA

**"He gives strength to the weary and increases
the power of the weak" (Isaiah 40:29).**

The outpatient department of Nazarene Hospital at Kudjip in Papua New Guinea (PNG) is a misshapen room too small for the crowd that fills it every weekday morning. The arrangement of the patients, both sitting and standing, implies chaos to the uninitiated. It's a source of consternation to those of us attempting to manage an orderly system. Within that crowd of patients are three groups. Some have minor complaints of trivial significance in terms of physical health. A second group has obvious and significant illnesses. Yet a third group harbors disease like a buried mine threatening to explode. It is this last group that creates the greatest challenge. It is this last group to which Lisa belonged.

Lisa was in her eighth month of pregnancy when she noted some bleeding. In her case our system worked well, and she was referred by the nurses to see a doctor. Ultrasonography showed the placenta was situated in a dangerous position, covering the outlet of the uterus. Normally the placenta is located high on the uterine wall, allowing the baby to deliver, followed by separation and delivery of the placenta. In Lisa's case, known as placenta previa, the onset of labor would mean separation of the placenta before the baby was born and life-threatening bleeding for both mother and baby.

I discussed the situation with Lisa and asked her to come into the hospital immediately for a Caesarean section. She declined for financial reasons and because her husband was not with her. (We ask about U.S. $20 for a Caesarean section, which is a great expense to our families without employment or income.)

I offered to waive the fees, but she refused to stay, though I made it clear to her that she could bleed to death if she went into labor outside the hospital. In Lisa's culture she needed her husband's consent before she could stay in the hospital—certainly before she could undergo surgery.

We saw nothing of Lisa during the following week. Each day I scanned the crowd in the outpatient department looking for the young pregnant mother with the dangerous condition. I informed my colleagues about Lisa, and we all watched and waited for her return.

On the seventh day we had other complications in the delivery room. A baby presenting feet first stuck in the birth canal. In an intense effort involving three doctors and a team of nurses, I divided the bones at the front of the mother's pelvis with a scalpel to create adequate space for delivery. We were too late. The newborn was in critical condition and lived only a few hours despite our efforts.

No sooner had this crisis been addressed than a second mother presented with the same problem, another double-footling breech. This time, however, the baby was not as low in the birth canal, allowing a brief window of opportunity to do a Caesarean section. I was thrilled to hear a strong cry from the baby after extracting him feetfirst through the surgical incision.

I FOUND LISA IN THE EMERGENCY ROOM, BARELY CONSCIOUS AND EXTREMELY PALE.

I was tired and drenched with sweat from the two demanding cases and the heat of the operating room (OR). As I exited the OR, looking forward to food, fluids, and a breather, missionary Dr. Susan Myers met me with the news that Lisa was back. She was in the emergency room in labor, bleeding and in shock. Her precarious situation was worsened by the fact that Dr. Jim Radcliffe, our excellent surgeon, was away. I am a left-handed family practice doctor with minimal surgical training and less aptitude. Lisa's condition demanded the best of surgical care, but the responsibility for her care had fallen on me.

I found Lisa in the ER, barely conscious and extremely pale. I couldn't feel a pulse in her wrist, further evidence of shock. Her husband wasn't with her, but a relative signed the consent for surgery, stating that Lisa had already died several times at home. (The distinction between loss of consciousness and death is not always clear in PNG culture and language.) Critical seconds ticked by as Lisa continued to bleed. We started two large intravenous lines and rushed to the operating room.

Ruth Perry and Paul Jeff, highly skilled anesthetists, provided rapid and effective anesthesia. Margaret Mugang, a tremendous scrub technician, has helped on thousands of emergency surgeries and played a key role in this one. There was no time for careful dissection. We sliced through layer after layer, including the placenta that lay between us and the baby's head. Blood poured from the uterine incision. I got my hand around the baby's head and lifted her from the lake of blood onto the drapes that covered her mother. We suctioned the fluids from the infant's nose and mouth and rejoiced to see her take her first breath. We removed the placenta, stopped the bleeding, and stabilized Lisa's desperate condition.

Lisa and her baby did very well. I scolded Lisa, once she and her baby were stable, about her refusal to come into the hospital until she had nearly died and was carried into the ER. She offered no response, and I was reminded how poorly I understand the world of my patients.

Cultural and financial factors led to a seven-day delay in the surgery that Lisa required, a delay that almost cost her and her baby their lives. I struggle with the realization that a young mother's life might depend on such things, especially when it involves issues of my adequacy and competence. When I focus on my competence, I become fearful and hesitant. When I put my trust in the Lord, my strength is renewed.

7

STEVEN

"Fear not, for I have redeemed you; I have called you by name; you are mine. When you pass through the waters, I will be with you" (Isaiah 43:1b-2a).

Coastal villagers were quietly going about their business in the evening hours of a Friday in July 1998. Fishermen pulled their canoes into the calm Sissano lagoon in northern PNG to unload their catch. Women prepared dinner from the pulp of palm trees, while watching their naked children play in the settling darkness.

Suddenly, disaster struck the four villages surrounding the lagoon. An abrupt three-foot shift of the ocean floor not far off the coast created an enormous tidal wave, or tsunami. According to one survivor, a deep rumbling noise resounded along the coast as the ocean first withdrew from the beaches, leaving for a moment a vast exposed stretch of ocean floor. Then the appalling surge of a 30-foot wall of water exploded onto the coast, demolishing every-

STEVEN WAS SWEPT VIOLENTLY OVER THE LAGOON, ACROSS THE SANDY BEACH, AND HURLED INTO THE DENSE UNDERGROWTH OF THE JUNGLE.

thing in its path. In that moment 2,000 people were swept into eternity. Several thousand others suffered injuries and lost their homes, their families, and their way of living.

Steven was an eight-year-old boy from an inland Sepik village. He and his father were visiting one of the coastal villages along the lagoon when the tsunami struck. Steven was swept violently over the lagoon, across the sandy beach, and hurled into the dense undergrowth of the jungle. He suffered a wound across the bridge of his nose and many abrasions. His father was killed, his body driven into the forked base of a large mangrove tree with such force that recovery workers, arriving the following day, were unable to extract it.

As word of the disaster spread, rescuers attempted to reach the wounded. Access to the site was hampered by the remote location and the total destruction of the single road with its bridges that served the area. Some were able to reach the site by descending through the jungle from higher elevations. As they did, they encountered coastal villagers retreating into the jungle, terrified and confused by the seemingly angry water that previously had been both their friend and source of livelihood. Those first witnesses discovered the carcasses of crocodiles, sea turtles, and deep-sea fish scattered in the jungle among the demolished villages and those killed or wounded, including little Steven.

Helicopters provided means for a more comprehensive assessment of the extent of the disaster. Bodies were seen across miles of coastline; others floated

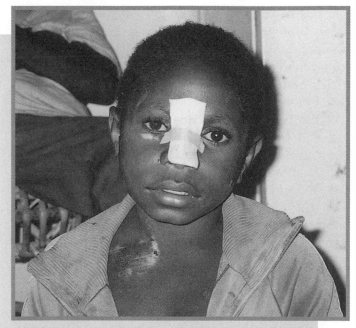

Steven treated for his facial injuries

out to sea with ocean currents. Soon the choppers were enlisted for the purpose of evacuating the wounded. Relief agencies hastily constructed camps and mobile hospitals, which promptly filled. The effort to recover bodies was halted after two days as the intense tropical heat and resultant decay created health hazards for the workers.

We in the Highlands did not hear of the catastrophe until the second morning after the tidal wave. News reached us via phone calls from friends and relatives in the United States. It was another full day before we were aware of the major extent of the disaster. We gathered medicines and supplies, collected food donations from our neighboring communities, and filled a Mission Aviation Fellowship (MAF) twin otter.

White Kintak, principal of our College of Nursing, and I accompanied the donated cargo for the flight to Aitape, the coastal town from which the relief effort was being coordinated. I sat in the copilot seat and enjoyed a remarkable view as we climbed over the mountains and descended over the vast swamps surrounding the mighty serpentine Sepik River. The gorgeous coastline seemed incongruous with the catastrophe of four days earlier and the ongoing struggle for those who had survived.

We delivered the donated food and supplies to the command post for the relief effort, then visited the hospital and listened to the accounts of the victims. Invariably they had suffered severe abrasions, similar to the road burn seen in motorcycle accidents. Many had fractures and internal injuries. All had lost loved ones. Many of the bodies were never found. We offered our consolation, our assurance, our prayers.

White and I joined a few Nazarene pastors from the Sepik area who had come to help in the recovery effort. They discovered Steven in one of the camps and realized he was from one of their churches and villages in the interior. We took responsibility for him, assuring the government relief workers that we would return him to his family.

For the next few days Steven stayed with us as we explored various ways of helping in the recovery efforts. Though Steven's physical injuries were not serious, his emotional wounds were obvious. He was frightened and withdrawn, refusing to go near the water. Whenever we had some free time, Steven and I looked at books, drew pictures, and played together. We worked on the alphabet and writing his name. Steven showed me how to harvest and drink the milk of coconuts.

Each day Steven showed signs of recovery. He began to express himself both in joy and tears. One evening less than a week after losing his father, Steven and I walked the beach together with our small group of pastors and laymen. During a pause, Steven knelt in the sand at the water's edge and began to build model villages out of driftwood. He had reconciled himself with the ocean waves and was ready to trust once again.

I later received radio confirmation that Steven was returned safely to his mother. She had received news of the tsunami but no word regarding her husband and son. She had assumed the worst for more than a week until the moment Steven appeared at her door. She was overwhelmed with joy that her son was home—alive and well.

8

SORI

**"And now these three remain, faith, hope,
and love" (1 Corinthians 13:13a).**

Sunrise over the Waghi Valley was announced by
the shrill wake-up call from a chorus of male cicadas.
A brief pause ensued, then another cacophony, as
flocks of rainbow lorikeets migrated through the
massive eucalyptus trees of Kudjip station. Wagtails
and honeyeaters followed with more amiable tunes
of their own. Low clouds and shifting morning light
adorned the magnificent mountains behind Nazarene
Hospital.

As the doctor on call this Sunday morning,
rounds began on the children's ward with the inten-
tion to eventually visit the sickest patients on each
of the four wards. As per the routine, I was joined by
the staff nurse and two nursing students. We made
our way down the row of closely spaced beds, each
bearing a tiny patient guarded by a watchful caring
mother.

Suddenly any semblance of calm routine evapo-
rated as a young father charged into the ward, desperation in his eyes, agony on his face, a lifeless body
draped across his arms. The panic in his expression
gave evidence of the immediacy of the loss.

"When did he quit breathing?" I asked.

"Just now," the man responded.

"Follow me." We raced to the emergency room in the remote chance of restoring life to the child.

A bag and mask for breathing. Chest compressions. Positioning of the child's head and neck. An instrument to visualize the vocal cords. Placement of a tube into the trachea. It is a rapid-fire scenario oft-repeated, hardly ever successful, especially in the highlands of Papua New Guinea (PNG). On this occasion—to our amazement and joy—the child opened his eyes and, after a few minutes, began to breathe weakly on his own.

Only then could I attend to the father's story. His son, Sori, had been well until the day before. On awakening Saturday morning, he had been too weak to walk. Sori's weakness worsened throughout the day, and by evening he had difficulty lifting his arms. His father carried him to the hospital on Saturday night, where the nurse had seen the child but found nothing specific on her examination other than weakness. The nurse had offered the father a place to sleep in the hospital so that Sori could be seen again Sunday morning. Able to muster only enough strength to survive the night, the boy had managed one final gasp and then collapsed in the moment before his father's frantic entry into the ward.

After listening to Dad's account, the severity of Sori's weakness became apparent. There was no trace of the usual flinch as our intravenous needle entered the vein of his arm. The boy's effort to breathe dwindled by the moment and soon faded altogether. We kept him alive by manually compressing the bag on his tracheal tube, delivering fresh oxygen with each squeeze of the fist.

Sori was the victim of a rapidly developing paralysis, a condition known as Guillain-Barré syndrome, with only facial expression and eye movements remaining. The cause of his illness was unknown. The treatment options for it were virtually nonexistent.

Complete paralysis, with no expectation of improvement in the near future, left this seven-year-old boy from the interior regions of PNG with little hope. Mind and spirit were still intact, but his body was isolated from his brain by this devastating disease of the nervous system.

FAMILY AND WORKERS AND VOLUNTEERS, ALL CLINGING TO A THREAD OF HOPE, TOOK TURNS SQUEEZING THE BAG THAT SUSTAINED THE LIFE OF THIS PRECIOUS CHILD.

We did not have a pediatric ventilator to breathe for him, and even if we had, we lacked the personnel with the expertise to care for a child with this condition. Furthermore, we didn't have the capability to perform blood gases, a lab test normally used to guide this kind of support. Instead, we depended upon the dad's interpretation of Sori's eyes and facial expression to make adjustments in the depth and rate of breathing. We recruited nurses and students and family members in an effort to keep Sori breathing. We canceled our Bible quizzing practice so that the teenage missionary kids could help, which they did eagerly. I called the larger hospitals around the country in search of a better solution for Sori but to no avail.

Complications are inevitable in this scenario; Sori's case was no exception. Frequent suctioning of secretions was critical, but we didn't have an adequate supply of sterile suction tubes. I shuddered when I discovered Sori's father reusing a suction tube that had fallen onto the dingy cement hospital floor.

On the third day in the hospital, Verne Ward Jr., one of our missionary kid high schoolers, came running to me in the outpatient clinic, "Dr. Bill, come quickly! Something is wrong with Sori!" We hurried to his bedside to find that the tube in the airway had become dislodged. We corrected the tube placement just as Sori threatened another complete arrest. There was a good chance that the tracheal tube would continue to give us difficulties, so Dr. Jim Radcliffe, our surgeon, performed a tracheotomy, creating a hole in Sori's neck for the tube delivering oxygen. For seven days and six nights without interruption, family and workers and volunteers, all clinging to a thread of hope, took turns squeezing the bag that sustained the life of this precious child. And we prayed.

On the seventh day, we received approval and made arrangements to transfer Sori to Port Moresby General Hospital, the teaching hospital in the capital city on the southern coast. The medical facility had space for Sori in their pediatric intensive care unit (PICU) and a ventilator.

Our major challenge was transportation. The Highlands are secluded from Port Moresby by a range of rugged mountains rising above 13,000 feet with no overland access. We chartered a flight with MAF out of the Hagen airport. The father would accompany Sori to Port Moresby; the mother would remain in the Highlands.

The first stage, Kudjip to Hagen, required a 45-minute ride over the deeply pitted surface of the Highlands Highway. We gently loaded Sori onto a stretcher, then into the ambulance, one person always attending to his breathing. The lack of adequate suction during transport was our primary concern, fearing that mucous secretions might block Sori's airway.

We were blessed with good weather as we arrived at the Hagen airport. Many hands assisted as we situated Sori into the reclined backseat of a six-seat Cessna. I sat beside him, continuing compressions of the bag. An oxygen tank and anesthetist Ruth Perry occupied the two seats in the middle row, Sori's father sat in front alongside the pilot. Sori's eyes searched mine, and I wondered how successful were my attempts to conceal my anxieties from him.

The 90-minute flight to Port Moresby took us over rugged mountains, dense tropical forests, and sheer river gorges. Most of the flight went smoothly, but at one point we encountered some clouds and moderate turbulence. The jostling of the plane altered the positioning of Sori's tubes, and my anxiety rose as it was suddenly difficult to support his breathing. Praying as I repositioned my patient and the tubes, I was grateful when the flow of air became easy once more.

An MAF van met us on the airstrip in muggy Port Moresby ready to transfer Sori to the hospital. Our entry with Sori on a stretcher with full ventilatory support caused some initial shock to the hospital staff. Soon, however, we were led to the PICU, where we connected Sori to the ventilator and met the staff who would be assuming his care. We prayed together and said good-bye to Sori and his father.

I had mixed emotions as we departed from the PICU where Sori and his father would remain. I was glad Sori was in the place where he had his best chance of surviving. But I found it difficult to relinquish the close ties that had bound us throughout the previous week.

For the next three weeks, Sori's condition did not change appreciably; he was totally dependent on the ventilator. Fed through a tube in his nose, he lost weight dramatically.

In his fourth week in Port Moresby, we were thrilled to receive the news that the disease had begun to release its grip on Sori. At first just a slight movement of his hand, then his arms, as well as some breathing efforts of his own. His doctor there gradually weaned him from the ventilator. Then a few days later, the hospital transferred Sori back to Kudjip after making special arrangements with a commercial airline.

Our elation with the return of our patient to Nazarene Hospital was tempered by Sori's wasted and fragile appearance. Had all our efforts been for naught? Would Sori succumb to pneumonia or another infection because of his poor nutritional status

Sori and his mother with Dr. Bill

and severe weakness even though his paralysis was improving?

The staff nurse and I settled him into the corner cubicle and discussed our plans for his treatment. As I exited the ward, I encountered Sori's mother, anxious to see her son. Her last contact had been more than a month earlier at Hagen airport when we had loaded Sori's motionless body, along with the necessary tubes and lines and equipment, onto the MAF flight bound for Port Moresby. Our security officer was now dutifully refusing her entry, because it wasn't visiting hours. I told the guard this time we must disregard our rules.

Sori's mother entered the ward fearfully, struggling to believe her son was still alive. Barefoot, simple wraparound dress, eyes cast down, leaning forward as if to force each step, she approached Sori's bed. As I withdrew the curtain to allow her entry, she cried aloud, took her last three steps without any hesitation, and threw her whole self onto Sori. She wept and held her son tightly, though he was still much too frail to return her embrace.

At the time of Sori's return to Kudjip, a Work and Witness team from the Sacramento District was serving at Kudjip, building a new laboratory. My parents were part of that team. Dad struck up a friendship with Sori and began the process of strengthening his wasted frame. It was often painful but completely necessary for Sori to break the cycle of weakness and inactivity. Sitting cross-legged on the floor, my father, the retired school teacher, played catch and created games to encourage and motivate the emaciated child.

AT THE FINAL VISIT, THE TRACHEOTOMY SCAR ON SORI'S NECK WAS THE ONLY PHYSICAL REMINDER OF HIS LONG ORDEAL.

Over time Sori rediscovered the use of his arms and legs. He could govern the muscles of his own body once again and was on his way to a full recovery. I saw him several times after his discharge from the hospital. At the final visit, the tracheotomy scar on Sori's neck was the only physical reminder of his long ordeal.

The name Sori comes from the English word *sorry*. I don't know why this name was chosen. He was the only son in his family, and he was obviously

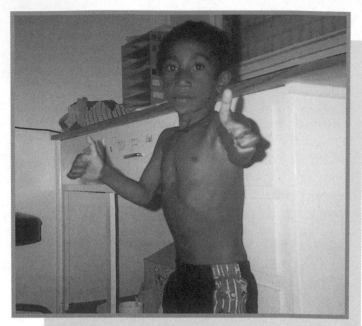
Sori, recovering and gaining strength

loved deeply by his parents. Sori's prognosis was
nearly hopeless, and we were fully cognizant from
the onset that the intense efforts we were making on
his behalf would likely be futile. Instead, God re-
stored Sori to us and to his family. With grateful
hearts, Sori's parents committed their lives to Christ
during his hospitalization.

The transient nature of our lives is portrayed in
Sori's story. Life and health, speech and breath, an
only son, all can evaporate in a moment. In the

midst of all that is fleeting, we do well to strengthen our grip on the realities of faith, hope, and love, those things that remain.

9
LUSAME

"A man with leprosy came and knelt before him
[Jesus] and said, 'Lord, if you are willing, you
can make me clean.' Jesus reached out his
hand and touched the man. 'I am willing,'
he said. 'Be clean!'" (Matthew 8:2-3a).

The odor filled the entire ward. Those who
could, exited quickly. The rest of us held cloths over
our noses to lessen the offense. At first glance it
seemed that she could not be alive. Sores covered
her entire body and invaded every orifice—deep
sores, dripping foul pus and blood. She was unable
to open her eyes because of the crusts that glued her
lids shut. Lying in her own stool, urine, pus, and
blood, unmoving except for shallow breathing, she
was hardly recognizable as a human being. This was
my introduction to Lusame.

This child of the PNG Highlands, about 12 years
old, had been taken by her parents to clinics and hospitals in another province for the past six months.
Starting as widespread blisters that had soon become
infected, the illness had sapped all the strength from
the girl and all the family resources in seeking help.
Lusame had been unable to sit or to stand for more
than four months and, by the time she was dropped
off at our hospital, she was comatose and nearly

dead. Apparently her family had given up all hope; none stayed with her upon her admission to the hospital.

We cleaned and bandaged Lusame's tiny wasted body, started her on antibiotics and steroids, gave her a blood transfusion, and prayed that God's will would be done in this child's life. It was hard to pray for healing, difficult to believe that Lusame could last another day. We prayed for ourselves that we would not just see the decay of the flesh but could have our eyes opened to a child of God's making.

THE GIRL LOOKED LIKE A MUMMY IN HER COCOON OF BANDAGES, BUT THE LIGHTS FLASHED ON IN HER EYES.

Remarkably, Lusame responded to our care and began to improve. As she emerged from her coma, she required anesthesia for her daily dressing changes. The girl looked like a mummy in her cocoon of bandages, but the lights flashed on in Lusame's eyes.

After a few days Lusame was able to speak. The sores of one arm, then the other, became dry enough that we could leave off the bandages. Lusame would become angry with me as I forced her to use her stiffened and wasted extremities that had not been utilized in more than four months. Every movement was painful but necessary if she were to regain strength and function.

With the gradual improvement, it became apparent that Lusame's sore-covered body had only been a disguise. In truth, here was a person, not unlike myself, with needs and desires and a will—in fact, a rather strong one!—who craved relief from suffering, protection from shame, recognition of her existence, and hope for a future.

Initially we fed Lusame through a tube from her nose to her stomach, but she improved enough to swallow. She liked boiled eggs and corned beef, so I kept a little money in my pocket to buy her lunch each day. Often I put Lusame in a wagon and took her outside to feel the sunshine and fresh air.

We rejoiced when Lusame could smile, feed herself, control her bowel movements, sit up, and eventually stand with support. We were grateful when we could reduce her bandage changes to every other day and when she no longer needed anesthesia for these changes. Lusame gained strength, and three months after she came to us, she could walk again. Adept at knitting, she often gave away her handiwork as gifts. She occupied her days visiting with national staff or missionary families in the hospital and in their homes.

We do not have a cure for Lusame's illness, which is probably a variation of a skin disorder known as pemphigus. We have done the research, consulted experts, and tried every potentially beneficial intervention available in PNG. At best, we are able to decrease her symptoms with long-term medications. Her medicines, however, have serious side effects and have significantly stunted her growth.

Lusame spent the better part of two years in the hospital. Her poor parents live far from the hospital, so they were unable to be with her most of the

Lusame *(left)*, responding to treatment

time. Attempts to treat her as an outpatient were met with frustration as she required intensive therapy and adjustments of her medications. Several times Lusame returned to the hospital with life-threatening relapses of her sickness. She has not returned for follow-up after her last discharge, and her present status is unknown.

Despite all the obvious differences, I marvel at the things I have in common with Lusame. This child from the bush, whose life has contained so much pain and suffering, shares, in essentials, the path of a middle-aged American physician.

Every life is lived somewhere between the extremes of joy and grief, between righteousness and unspeakable evil, between purposefulness and meaninglessness, between peace and turmoil, between hope and despair, between gratefulness and bitterness, between loving and hating, between loneliness and belonging. Our choices and responses to the grace of God determine where we dwell within those parameters. These are the issues of the soul, and they are fundamental to what we are, much more so than our education, achievements, acquisitions, reputation, health, or life span. These are the issues that bind me to Lusame.

10
EASTER

**"I [Jesus] am the resurrection and the life.
He who believes in me will live,
even though he dies" (John 11:25).**

As I arrived at our home, Marsha met me at the door with a look of concern and an urgent message to call Carol. Dr. Carol Howard is a family practice physician who is gifted in the area of obstetrics. She and her husband, Bob, also a physician, were taking call for the weekend.

I phoned Carol, but the sorrow in her voice was far too great to be addressed over the phone. I hurried to the hospital and found Carol and Bob in one of the offices. Carol, her words interspersed with tears, shared with me the events of the past 12 hours.

Our nurses had called Dr. Carol around 1 A.M. to inform her that we had an expectant mother in labor, but that the baby's hand had entered the birth canal before the head. When this occurs, the shoulder and the head of the infant become tightly wedged in the mother's pelvis and cannot be delivered normally.

Carol awakened and summoned the surgical team to the operating room, believing this mother would require Caesarean section. Before operating, however, Carol examined the mother again and was surprised to discover that the baby had withdrawn her hand.

The baby's position was now normal with her head first, so the surgery was canceled. The mother was returned to the delivery room for monitoring of her labor. Carol and the surgical team returned to their homes and tried to sleep.

The next call came around 7 A.M. The baby's hand was once again in the birth canal. This time, however, there were further complications. The mother was no longer feeling any movement from the baby, and the nurses could not hear the baby's heartbeat. Carol hurried to the hospital, desperately hoping that the ominous reports were misleading. She did an ultrasound scan in an attempt to see movement or detect a heartbeat. Sadly, neither were present.

TURNING THE BABY AROUND, I DELIVERED HER FEETFIRST.

In a strictly medical sense, Carol had made the right decisions, but she was devastated by the loss. In addition, it was still necessary to do the operation because of the malpresentation of the baby. A Caesarean section without a live baby is technically the same operation, but emotionally there is a world of difference. Before I was involved, Carol had already performed the difficult task of informing the family of the baby's death and the need to proceed with surgery.

Knowing how Carol was feeling, I offered to do the C-section. The surgical team was ready and the mother received a spinal anesthetic. Before operating we prayed, as we always do. This time we included petitions for Dr. Carol and comfort for the family.

As soon as I made the uterine incision, the baby's elbow protruded from the wound. I pushed the elbow back into the uterus in an attempt to grasp the baby's head, but without success. The infant's arm continued to foil my attempt to accomplish a headfirst delivery. I reversed directions, reached high in the uterus, and found both ankles. Turning the baby around, I delivered her feetfirst.

I thought I felt a slight movement at the ankle but discounted the sensation as a trick of my own imagination and wishful thinking. I still thought my eyes were deceiving me when I laid the baby onto the drapes and noticed a twitch of the baby's chin. Then it was repeated. I glanced at Margaret, the scrub nurse, to see whether she was seeing the same thing, and I caught the excitement in her eyes. "This baby is alive! Mom, your baby is alive! Somebody call Carol!"

The baby was crying and strong within a few minutes. There were no apparent complications. What a precious melody is a newborn cry. Every childbirth is a wonder and a miracle. This one took us closer to the appropriate response—buckled knees —than most. If this baby had been mine to name, I would have called her *Easter.*

Epilogue

In Africa and Papua New Guinea mothers do
not name their babies until the infants are several
weeks—even some months—old. When there is a
good chance that the baby will not survive, the naming is postponed. To name someone is to recognize
him or her as a person, to invest in her or his life, to
enter into relationship, and thus to become vulnerable. Therefore, a name involves risk.

The pain, tears, and dying of another touches
my own life.

Like these hesitant mothers, we may be reluctant
to name the people in our world, to identify with
them, to expose ourselves to their suffering. We might
be overwhelmed by their misery, but God isn't.

"When he [Jesus] saw the crowds, he had compassion on them" (Matthew 9:36*a*). When Jesus
looks at crowds, He sees people—people with
names, dreams, hopes, needs, fears. Jesus sees Nelisiwe, Sori, Lusame, Mazwi, Mabhayoyo, Frank Joe, and
all the rest of us. He knows each of us by name. And
when we suffer, He is moved with deep compassion.

The heart of God is bound to His people in inti-
mate relationship. He is always redeeming, always
saving, always rescuing. He is neither tired nor

weary. The redemptive, healing activity of God surrounds us. We are the recipients of God's grace and the objects of His mercy.

But the ramifications of our close relationship with God extend beyond the precious gifts we receive. We have the privilege of participating in the work of God. We are invited to share the Good News and perform works of service, to be directly involved in God's response to the brokenness of this world. While doing so, we have His promise of strength for the task, His offer of joy and peace throughout the journey.

> NAMING THE PEOPLE IN OUR WORLD MEANS WE ARE READY TO TASTE THE BITTERNESS OF THEIR FALLING TEARS AND FEEL THE AGONY OF THEIR BROKEN HEARTS.

Our readiness to offer ourselves to such a mission requires a willingness to view people as God views them, to know them as God knows them, to love them as God loves them. Strangers take on names and faces.

Naming the people in our world means we are ready to taste the bitterness of their falling tears and feel the agony of their broken hearts. It means we will allow their despair to compromise our comfort and their anguish to diminish our calm.

If we choose to ignore the hurting people surrounding us, we protect ourselves from their misery. But at what cost? When we isolate and insulate ourselves, not only do we forfeit the opportunity to share in their victories, their healing, and their joys,

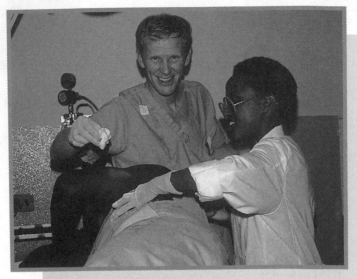
Dr. Bill in emergency room

we also depart from the very path on which we encounter Jesus. Whether we find ourselves in a mission hospital in Swaziland or the bush of Papua New Guinea—or wherever people are hurting—we find a Savior.

Pronunciation Guide

The following information will assist in pronouncing some unfamiliar words in this book. The suggested pronunciations, though not always precise, are close approximations of the way the terms are pronounced.

Aitape	IE-tah-pay
Baragwanath	bair-uh-GWAH-nuhth
Guillain-Barré	GEE-lan-bah-RAY
Hagen	HAH-gun
Kintak	kihn-TAHK
Kudjip	KOO-jihp
Lusame	loo-SAH-mee
Mabhayoyo	mah-bah-YOH-yoh
Matsapa	maht-SAH-puh
Manzini	mahn-ZEE-nee
Mazwi	MAH-zwee
Moresby	MOHRZ-bee
Mugang	moo-GANG
Nelisiwe	neh-lee-SEE-weh
Sepik	SEE-pihk
Sissano	sih-SAH-noh
Siswati	see-SWAH-tee
Sori	SAH-ree
tsunami	soo-NAH-mee
Soweto	soh-WEH-toh
Waghi	WAH-gee